**Quick Start Guides**

D1635431

The New Essential
BLOOD SUGAR
DIET
COOKBOOK

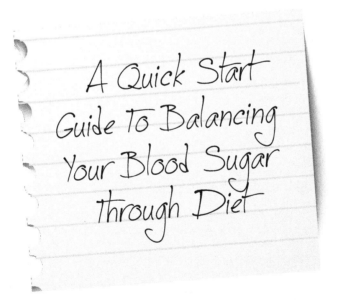

A Quick Start Guide To Balancing Your Blood Sugar Through Diet

Improve Your Health And Lose Weight
PLUS Over 80 New Blood Sugar Friendly Recipes

First published in 2016 by Erin Rose Publishing

Text and illustration copyright © 2016 Erin Rose Publishing

Design: Julie Anson

ISBN: 978-0-9933204-9-1

A CIP record for this book is available from the British Library.

DISCLAIMER: This book is for informational purposes only and not intended as a substitute for the medical advice, diagnosis or treatment of a physician or qualified healthcare provider. The reader should consult a physician before undertaking a new health care regime and in all matters relating to his/her health, and particularly with respect to any symptoms that may require diagnosis or medical attention.

While every care has been taken in compiling the recipes for this book we cannot accept responsibility for any problems which arise as a result of preparing one of the recipes. The author and publisher disclaim responsibility for any adverse effects that may arise from the use or application of the recipes in this book. Some of the recipes in this book include nuts and eggs. If you have an egg or nut allergy it's important to avoid these.

CONTENTS

Introduction..1

How To Get Started!..2

Finding Hidden Sugars 3

Curbing Your Sweet Tooth..4

Cooking For Better Blood Sugar 6

Recipes Under 100 Calories

Spiced Bean Balls...8

Basil & Tomato Olives 8

Carrot & Orange Soup...9

Kale & Butter Bean Soup...10

Cauliflower Rice...11

Spanish Rice 12

Blackbean Hummus 13

Basil & Lemon Hummus With Celery................................13

Blueberry, Coconut & Chia Seed Pudding........................14

Strawberry & Chia Seed Pudding 14

Macadamia & Coconut Bites 15

Macaroons 16

Ginger & Lime Refresher 17

Recipes Under 200 Calories

Chocolate & Banana Smoothie..20

Greek Green Smoothie...20

Superfood Juice 21

Creamy Berry Smoothie...21

Goats' Cheese Stuffed Cherry Tomatoes 22

Bean & Vegetable Soup..23

Roasted Red Pepper Soup 24

Pea & Ham Soup...25

Tomato & Lentil Soup...26

Curried Pumpkin Seeds...27

Mushroom Stroganoff...28

Chickpea, Lemon & Coriander Salad..29

Garlic & Herb King Prawns 30

Cashew Crust Kale Chips 31

Cheddar & Spinach Mini Omelettes 32

Fish Casserole..33

Spicy Roast Chickpeas..34

Rhubarb & Ginger Compote With Greek Yogurt 35

Peanut Butter Frozen Yogurt...36

Low Carb Chocolate Brownies..37

Chocolate Chip Peanut Butter Cookies 38

Raspberry Panna Cotta...39

Recipes Under 300 Calories

Pesto & Mozzarella Stuffed Mushrooms....................................42

Green Goodness Smoothie...42

Chunky Chicken & Vegetable Soup 43

Oregano & Lemon Roast Chicken 44

Parmesan & Courgette (Zucchini) Bake 45

Feta Cheese & Butter Bean Salad 46

Lemon Breadcrumb Prawns..47

Smoked Pork & Vegetable Skewers 48

Paprika Prawn Tapas...49

Slow Cooker Vegetable Dahl 50

Prawn & Spinach Omelette...51

Spiced Mackerel..52

Thai Chicken Soup 53

Tuna & Chickpea Salad 54

Quick Bean Chilli 55

Slow Cooked Beef Curry..56

Asparagus & Poached Egg 57

Chicken Cacciatore 58

Chicken Fajitas, Salsa & Lettuce Wrap......................................59

Spinach, Blue Cheese & Walnut Salad..60

Chocolate Mousse 61

Recipes Under 400 Calories

Moroccan Tuna Steaks 64

Turkey & Chickpea Balls 65

Smoked Salmon & Pesto 'Spaghetti' 66

Aubergine & Lentil Bake..67

Rosemary Chicken & Roast Vegetables 68

Parsley & Lemon Salmon 69

Lentil & Bacon Soup..70

Green Lentil Curry 71

Mexican Chunky Soup..72

Beef Goulash 73

Turkish Eggs 74

Eggs With Carrot & Bacon Hash 75

BLT Chicken Salad..76

Sausage & Kale Stir-Fry 77

Spiced Citrus & Olive Pork 78

Lamb Skewers & Yogurt Dip 79

Tandoori Salmon 80

Recipes Under 550 Calories

Mustard Lime Turkey & Butter Bean Mash...82

Chinese Chicken Salad 83

Chicken, Cannellini & Almond Bake 84

High Protein Blueberry Pancakes 85

Chicken & Avocado Wraps...86

Chicken Goujons..87

Pine Nut & Avocado Courgetti...88

Chunky Lamb Stew 89

Sirloin Steak & Chimchurri Sauce..90

Halloumi Mushroom & Tomato Kebabs 91

Avocado Fries 92

Chickpea & Chorizo Casserole...93

Southern Pork & Beans 94

INTRODUCTION

Whether you decide to make improvements to your diet because you have existing blood sugar problems, for weight loss or to protect your health, it can be daunting to know what to eat. In this book, our aim is to present what you can eat to attain better health in a straightforward way so that you can eat a healthier diet, improve your blood sugar and lose weight. You will be able to take positive steps to improve your health that help put you in control of your weight and nip disease in the bud. Prevention has always been better than cure so if you are ready to get started, read on!

It can be confusing working out what to cook, that's why we bring you a complete selection of calorie-counted recipes that cater for every meal so you don't have to spend your time doing it. There is plenty of scientific research in existence as to why cutting out sugar and reducing your carbohydrate intake is good for your health so these healthy and tasty meal suggestions are the perfect, time-saving accompaniment to make eating to balance your blood sugar, quick, easy and very very tasty.

The recipes in this book are a combination of meals for 1,2 or 4 people so it's useful whether you are cooking just for one or a larger group, plus many of the meals can be frozen so you can cook batches when you have the time and energy for such times as when you don't!

All recipes are categorised by calorie content which is great if you are restricting your calorie intake. Plus, they are interchangeable for each meal or snack, so you can always find a light bite, snack or meal for any time of the day.

How To Get Started!

There really is no time like the present so get started straight away! Take a look at the foods to avoid and familiarise yourself with the list so that you're well prepared.

REDUCE or **AVOID** all products containing sugar and starchy carbohydrates, such as:

- Cakes, muesli, granola, biscuits, cookies, breakfast cereal, cereal bars, syrup, honey, chocolate, sweets and candy. Marinades, dressings and ready-made sauces such as ketchup, sweet chilli sauce, barbecue sauce and any dressing or processed foods containing sugar. Remember to read the label to check for hidden sugars too (see section).

- Avoid dried fruit, like apricots, mango, pineapple and figs.

- Starchy carbohydrates such as bread, rice cakes, crackers, pasta, potatoes, sweet potatoes, brown and white rice.

- Beware of fruit juices, milk shakes, smoothies, fizzy drinks, cocktails and drinks containing sugar and concentrated fruit juice.

- If you usually have oat or rice milk, opt for a high protein low carb milk like almond or hazelnut milk.

Decide what you want to get out of the diet. Are you a healthy weight and looking to safeguard your long-term health or are you at risk of diabetes or a type 2 diabetic with excess weight? You can make changes by reducing or avoiding sugars and starchy carbohydrates from your diet or if you want to maximise the benefits and lose excess pounds, you can additionally reduce your calorie intake. If you choose to limit your calorie intake, aim to consume no more than 1000 calories a day. Reducing your calorie intake will improve weight loss and speed up the shedding of excess belly fat so you'll achieve more rapid results while improving your blood sugar.

Finding Hidden Sugars

Always read the labels on everything you buy at the supermarket. This sounds simple but you'd be surprised how easy it is to load up your shopping basket with foods you didn't realise contain sugar or derivatives of sugar.

Check out the list of names sugar is also known as and do your best to avoid these.

- Invert sugar syrup
- Cane juice crystals
- Dextrin
- Dextrose
- Glucose syrup
- Sucrose
- Fructose syrup
- Maltodextrin
- Barley malt
- Beet sugar
- Corn syrup
- Date sugar
- Palm sugar
- Malt syrup
- Dehydrated fruit juice
- Fruit juice concentrate
- Carob syrup
- Golden syrup
- Refiners syrup
- Ethylmaltol

Curbing Your Sweet Tooth

It's not just the effects of sugar that see-saw your body's blood sugar and cause sugar cravings. Starchy carbs also sharply elevate blood sugar levels then leave you feeling tired and depleted. Research has shown that even eating sweet tasting foods can trigger sugar cravings as part of the brain is activated by the sweet taste, stimulating the desire for more. For this reason it's best not to give in to cravings to really get them under control. For some people this may only be 4-5 days and for others it could take weeks.

Using sweeteners can be helpful in the beginning if you diet is loaded with sugars and starchy carbohydrates but if cravings continue and you lust for something sweet, consider reducing your use of sweeteners even temporarily. Stevia is a natural sweetener and shows none of the side effects associated with artificial sweeteners.

If you get a craving, opt for something with protein or healthy fats, because fats are satisfying and reduce your appetite in a way that sugar never can do. Keep a supply of suitable snacks available; cubes of cheese, nuts, full-fat yogurt or cooked chicken.

Distraction is also a good tactic. If you've had a meal and have that longing for something sweet, do something that takes you away from the kitchen. Take a walk, have a bath or drink a large glass of water or your favourite herbal tea.

You can take a look at the recipes and choose something you really like the sound of which you can prepare in advance, or you can have the ingredients handy to rustle up a meal or snack in a hurry.

Snacking through boredom is something most of us have done, it's just recognising when you go looking in the cupboards that you aren't actually hungry you just want something to do. Once you recognise it you can do something else, read a magazine or get some exercise.

Comfort eating as a pick-me-up or to stifle anxiety is a vicious cycle, especially if you reach for chocolate bars, cakes or stodgy white bread, which let's face it, that's what we are drawn to as a mood fixer. Not only does it pile on the pounds but the highs and lows of the blood sugar change can lead to low mood and anxiety and so it begins all over again.

Be your own best friend and don't put temptation in your way. Before you begin, clear your cupboards of all sugary foods and replace them with healthy alternatives like nuts and seeds. Nuts are a great source of magnesium which is helpful for stress and depression, which is going to make life easier all round.

Fruit Sugars

Fruit has a great many benefits. It can also contain large amounts of sugar so be wary of how much fruit you eat. Aim for low sugar fruits and in moderation only. Many people find that eating a piece of sweet fruit on its own can make you feel even more hungry 30 minutes later, so to avoid spiking your blood sugar by having fruit on its own as a snack in between meals, try adding it at mealtimes instead, alongside cheese, nuts or greek yogurt.

Check with your GP or healthcare professional before making significant dietary or lifestyle changes to ensure there are no underlying issues and especially if you have an existing medical condition or are currently taking any medication. Regular check-ups to review medication may be beneficial.

Cooking For Better Blood Sugar

Firstly, we want you to enjoy your food and giving up sugar and going low carb can be a big deal, especially if your diet is currently not the best. There will be a short period of adjustment while your taste buds get used to the change in flavours, especially subtler flavours as sugar is a strong and over-whelming taste.

The sweet recipes in this book are to be eaten in moderation only occasionally and remember stimulating your sweet tooth can result in you giving in to further temptation.

The recipes in this book are categorised by their calorie count so you can swap around what you have for breakfast, lunch and dinner and choose meals based on their calorie content to stay within your calorie restrictions.

If you're including chocolate, make sure it's good quality dark chocolate with a high cocoa content. Chocolate itself is good for you, it's the large quantity of sugar that's added to it that is the real problem.

Eating a large portion of carbohydrates basically has the same effect as sugar does, so swapping the carb portion of meals for an equivalent portion of vegetables is a much better alternative.

Don't underestimate the value of leftovers from the night before. They can be a quick and satisfying meal the next day. If you are only cooking for yourself you can still follow a recipe for 4 and freeze the remaining portions ready for another day.

We hope you enjoy the recipes! Wishing you great health!

Recipes Under 100 Calories

Spiced Bean Balls

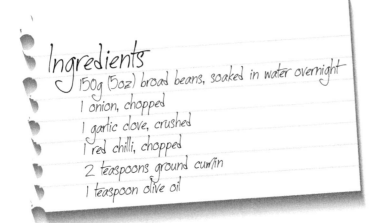

Ingredients
- 150g (5oz) broad beans, soaked in water overnight
- 1 onion, chopped
- 1 garlic clove, crushed
- 1 red chilli, chopped
- 2 teaspoons ground cumin
- 1 teaspoon olive oil

MAKES 12

15 calories per ball

Method

Place all of the ingredients into a food processor and blend to a smooth paste. Shape the mixture into balls and place them on a greased baking tray. Transfer them to the oven and bake at 180C/360F for 20 minutes.

Basil & Tomato Olives

Ingredients
- 50g (2oz) pitted green olives
- 1 tablespoon fresh basil, chopped
- 1 tomato, chopped
- 1 clove of garlic chopped
- Black pepper

SERVES 1

84 calories per serving

Method

Place all of the ingredients into a bowl and mix well. Chill before serving.

Carrot & Orange Soup

Ingredients

450g (1lb) carrots, chopped
3 tablespoons fresh parsley, plus extra
for garnish
2 onions, chopped
1 courgette (zucchini), chopped
1 tablespoon olive oil
1200mls (2 pints) hot water
Grated zest and juice of 1 orange

**MAKES
4**

96
calories
per serving

Method

Heat the oil in a saucepan, add the onions and cook for 5 minutes. Add in the carrots and courgette (zucchini) and cook for 5 minutes. Stir in the orange zest and hot water. Reduce the heat and simmer for 10 minutes. Stir in the parsley and orange juice. Using a hand blender or food processor blend the soup until smooth. Re-heat if necessary before serving. Serve with a sprinkling of parsley.

Kale & Butter Bean Soup

Ingredients

200g (7oz) kale
125g (4oz) butter beans
2 carrots, peeled and diced
1 stick celery
1 medium onion, peeled and chopped
1 clove of garlic, crushed
1 teaspoon olive oil
600mls (1 pint) vegetable stock (broth)
Sea salt
Freshly ground black pepper

**MAKES
4**

97
calories
per serving

Method

Heat the olive oil in a large saucepan and the garlic and vegetables, apart from the kale and butter beans. Stir for 2-3 minutes on a medium heat. Add the stock (broth) and bring to boil. Reduce and cook for 15 minutes. Blend half the butter beans and add to the soup. Add the kale, the remaining butter beans and cook for 10 minutes. This soup can be blended smooth or left chunky if you prefer. Season with salt and pepper then serve.

Cauliflower Rice

Ingredients

1 head of cauliflower, broken into florets
2 tablespoons olive oil
Sea salt
Freshly ground black pepper

MAKES 6

70 calories per serving

Method

Place the cauliflower into a food processor and blitz it until it becomes small rice-like pieces. Heat the oil in a large frying pan and add the cauliflower. Cook for around 5 minutes or until softened. Season with salt and pepper. Serve as an alternative to rice, potatoes or pasta as a great accompaniment to meats and salads. It's so easy to jazz up basic cauliflower rice with a teaspoon of paprika or curry powder or mushrooms and chorizo to make a stand alone light meal or to go alongside curries and casseroles.

Spanish Rice

Ingredients

1 head of cauliflower, broken into florets.
2 carrots, peeled and roughly chopped
250g (9oz) tomato passata or tinned chopped tomatoes
2 tablespoons olive oil
1 teaspoon chilli powder
1 teaspoon cumin
Small handful of coriander (cilantro)

SERVES
6

91
calories
per serving

Method

Place the cauliflower and carrots into a food processor and blitz until fine and rice-like. Heat the olive oil in a large frying pan, add the cauliflower and carrots and cook for 5-7 minutes or until the vegetables have softened. Add the tomato passata, chilli and cumin and warm it through. Sprinkle in the coriander (cilantro) just before serving.

Blackbean Hummus

Ingredients
- 400g (14oz) tin black beans
- 1 1/2 tablespoons tahini paste (sesame seed paste)
- 1 clove garlic
- 1/2 teaspoon ground cumin
- 1/2 teaspoon sea salt
- 1/4 teaspoon cayenne pepper
- 1/4 teaspoon paprika
- 2 tablespoons water
- 2 tablespoons lemon juice

SERVES 6

97 calories per serving

Method

Place all of the ingredients and process until smooth. Serve as a dip for vegetable crudités or use with salads.

Basil & Lemon Hummus With Celery

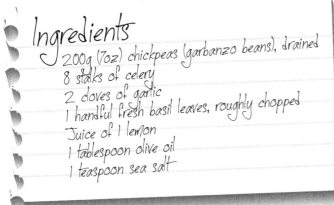

Ingredients
- 200g (7oz) chickpeas (garbanzo beans), drained
- 8 stalks of celery
- 2 cloves of garlic
- 1 handful fresh basil leaves, roughly chopped
- Juice of 1 lemon
- 1 tablespoon olive oil
- 1 teaspoon sea salt

SERVES 4

94 calories per serving

Method

Place all of the ingredients, except the celery, into a food processor and process until smooth. Serve as a dip for the celery stalks.

Blueberry, Coconut & Chia Seed Pudding

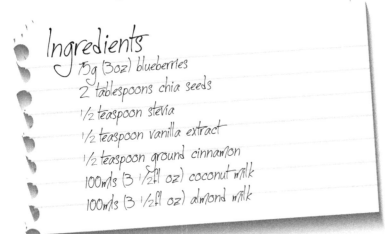

Ingredients
- 75g (3oz) blueberries
- 2 tablespoons chia seeds
- 1/2 teaspoon stevia
- 1/2 teaspoon vanilla extract
- 1/2 teaspoon ground cinnamon
- 100mls (3 1/2fl oz) coconut milk
- 100mls (3 1/2fl oz) almond milk

MAKES 4

79 calories per serving

Method
Place the coconut milk, almond milk, stevia and vanilla extract into a bowl and mix until smooth. Add the chia seeds and stir. Transfer the mixture to 4 dessert glasses or small bowls. Chill the fridge for 1-2 hours and the mixture has thickened to look like rice pudding. Sprinkle on the cinnamon and scatter the blueberries on top. Enjoy. These delicious little puddings can be stored in the fridge for 2-3 days.

Strawberry & Chia Seed Pudding

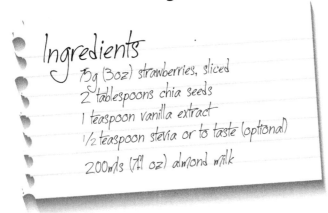

Ingredients
- 75g (3oz) strawberries, sliced
- 2 tablespoons chia seeds
- 1 teaspoon vanilla extract
- 1/2 teaspoon stevia or to taste (optional)
- 200mls (7fl oz) almond milk

SERVES 2

83 calories per serving

Method
Place the chia seeds and almond milk in a bowl and mix well. Cover them and place them in the fridge for 1-2 hours or overnight. In the morning add in the strawberries, vanilla and stevia (if using) and serve into bowls.

Macadamia & Coconut Bites

Ingredients

125g (4oz) almond butter
75g (3oz) desiccated (shredded) coconut
75g (3oz) macadamia nuts, chopped
2 tablespoons tahini paste (sesame seed paste)
1 teaspoon stevia sweetener (or more to taste)
Extra coconut for rolling

MAKES
approx. 24

84
calories
each

Method

Place the desiccated (shredded) coconut, tahini (sesame seed paste), almond butter and chopped macadamia nuts into a bowl and combine them thoroughly. Stir in a teaspoon of stevia powder then taste to check the sweetness. Add a little more sweetener if you wish. Roll the mixture into balls. Scatter some desiccated (shredded) coconut on a plate and coat the balls in it. Keep them refrigerated until ready to use.

Macaroons

Ingredients

250g (9oz) desiccated (shredded) coconut
4 egg whites
1 ½ tablespoons stevia (or to taste)
Seeds of 1 vanilla pod

MAKES
approx. 20

79
calories
per serving

Method

Whisk the egg whites in a large bowl, until they form still peaks. Add in the vanilla and coconut and combine all of the ingredients. Line a baking sheet with parchment paper. Use a teaspoon and scoop out some mixture, rolling it into a small ball. Place it on the baking sheet and repeat for the remaining mixture. Transfer it to the oven and bake at 180C/360F for around 12 minutes or until the macaroons are golden.

Ginger & Lime Refresher

Ingredients

200mls (7fl oz) coconut water
Juice of 1/4 of a lime
1cm (1/2 inch) chunk of ginger, finely
chopped

**SERVES
1**

40
calories
per serving

Method

Mix all of the ingredients in a glass and add a few ice cubes. Drink straight away. This makes a lovely refreshing drink which keeps hunger away.

Recipes Under 200 Calories

Chocolate & Banana Smoothie

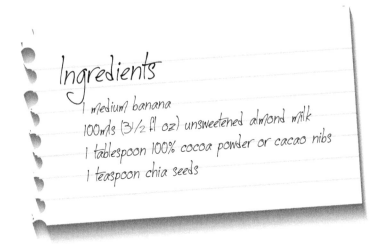

Ingredients

1 medium banana
100mls (3½ fl oz) unsweetened almond milk
1 tablespoon 100% cocoa powder or cacao nibs
1 teaspoon chia seeds

SERVES
1

169
calories
per serving

Method

Place all the ingredients into a food processor and mix until smooth and creamy.

Greek Green Smoothie

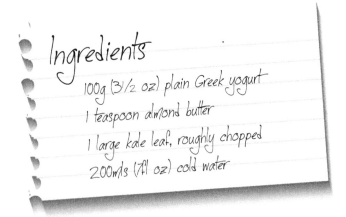

Ingredients

100g (3½ oz) plain Greek yogurt
1 teaspoon almond butter
1 large kale leaf, roughly chopped
200mls (7fl oz) cold water

SERVES
1

173
calories
per serving

Method

Place all of the ingredients into a blender and process until it's smooth. Pour and enjoy! This smoothie is particularly satisfying so it makes a great meal replacement.

Superfood Juice

Ingredients

- 2 celery stalks
- 3 large kale leaves
- 1 cucumber
- 1 apple
- 1 teaspoon chopped parsley
- 2cm (1 inch) chunk of ginger, peeled
- 1 lemon
- 1/4 teaspoon cinnamon (optional)

SERVES
1

131
calories
per serving

Method

Juice all the ingredients together, except the cinnamon and pour the juice into a tall glass. Stir in the cinnamon and drink immediately. You can add a few ice cubes for a really refreshing drink.

Creamy Berry Smoothie

Ingredients

- 50g (2oz) frozen blueberries
- 50g (2oz) frozen strawberries
- 125g (4oz) plain unflavoured yogurt
- 100mls (3½ oz) unsweetened soya milk

SERVES
1

162
calories
per serving

Method

Whizz the berries, yogurt and soya milk together in a blender and process until smooth.

Goats' Cheese Stuffed Cherry Tomatoes

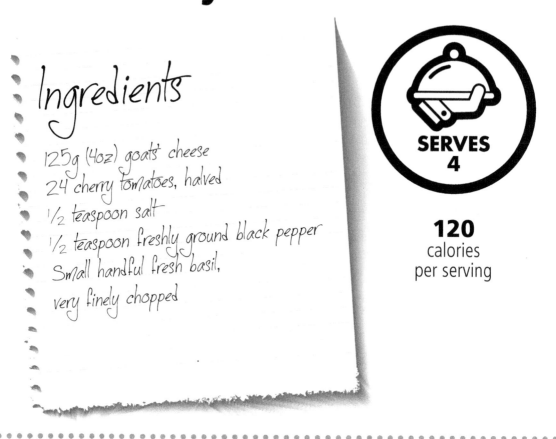

Ingredients

125g (4oz) goats' cheese
24 cherry tomatoes, halved
½ teaspoon salt
½ teaspoon freshly ground black pepper
Small handful fresh basil, very finely chopped

SERVES 4

120 calories per serving

Method

Place the goats' cheese in a bowl and mix in the chopped basil. Season with salt and black pepper. Gently scoop the tomato seeds and pulp out from inside the tomatoes and pour out any juice. Using a teaspoon scoop some of the cheese mixture into each tomato. Place them on a decorative plate and serve.

Bean & Vegetable Soup

Ingredients

200g (7oz) frozen soya beans (also called edamame beans)
200g (7oz) frozen peas
50g (2oz) rocket (arugula) leaves
6 spring onions (scallions), trimmed and chopped
1 small bunch basil leaves, chopped
450mls (15fl oz) hot vegetable stock (broth)
300mls (½ pint) milk or soya milk

SERVES 4

160 calories per serving

Method

Put the soya beans, peas, vegetable stock (broth) and spring onions (scallions) into a saucepan. Bring it to the boil and simmer for five minutes. Add the basil and rocket (arugula) leaves and soya milk. Pour half of the soup mixture into a food processor and process until smooth. If using a hand blender pour half the soup into a bowl and blitz until creamy. Return the blended soup to the saucepan and warm it through. Serve and enjoy.

Roasted Red Pepper Soup

Ingredients

6 large tomatoes, peeled
4 large red peppers (bell peppers)
4 garlic cloves, unpeeled
1 teaspoon dried oregano
1 red onion, peeled and chopped
900mls (1½ pints) vegetable stock (broth)
Handful of fresh basil leaves
1 tablespoon olive oil

SERVES 4

116 calories per serving

Method

Place the peppers on a baking tray and roast them in the oven at 200C/400F for 30-35 minutes until the skin blisters. Place them in a sealable plastic bag until they're cool. Remove them and peel off the skin and throw away the seeds. Heat the olive oil in a large pan, add the onion and garlic and cook for 5 minutes until it has softened. Chop the tomatoes and add them to the saucepan along with the peppers, oregano, stock (broth) and a few basil leaves. Simmer for 30 minutes. Using a hand blender or food processor blitz the soup until smooth. Serve with a garnish of chopped basil leaves.

Pea & Ham Soup

Ingredients

650g (1lb 7 oz) frozen peas, defrosted

175g (6oz) roast ham or chopped ham hock

1 onion, chopped

3 tablespoons fresh mint, chopped

1 litre (1½ pints) vegetable or chicken stock (broth)

1 tablespoon olive oil

Sea salt

Freshly ground black pepper

SERVES 6

147 calories per serving

Method

Heat the oil in a saucepan, add the onion and cook for 5 minutes until the onion softens. Add in the peas, mint and stock (broth) and cook for 10 minutes. Using a hand blender or food processor blitz the soup until creamy. Stir in the ham and season with salt and pepper. Return it to the heat if necessary. Serve into bowls.

Tomato & Lentil Soup

Ingredients

175g (6oz) red lentils
400g (14oz) tinned chopped tomatoes
2 teaspoons tomato purée
4 tablespoons plain Greek yoghurt
2 celery sticks, chopped
1 onion, peeled and chopped
1 carrot, peeled and chopped
1 garlic clove, crushed
1 teaspoon ground cumin
½ teaspoon ground coriander (cilantro)
1.2 litres vegetable stock (broth)
1 tablespoon olive oil

SERVES 4

187
calories
per serving

Method

Heat the oil in a saucepan and add the onion. Cook for 5 minutes until the onion softens. Add in the celery and carrot and cook for 2 minutes, stirring occasionally. Add the garlic, cumin and coriander (cilantro) and cook for a further minute. Add in the stock (broth), lentils, tomatoes and tomato purée and cook for 20-30 minutes. Using a hand blender or food processor blend the soup until smooth and creamy. Serve into bowls with a swirl of yogurt. Enjoy.

Curried Pumpkin Seeds

Ingredients

300g (11oz) pumpkin seeds
1/2 teaspoon sea salt
1/2 teaspoon mild curry powder
1 tablespoon olive oil

SERVES
12

151
calories
per serving

Method

Place the olive oil, curry powder and salt into a bowl and stir well. Add the pumpkin seeds to the bowl and coat them in the mixture. Scatter the pumpkin seeds on a baking sheet. Transfer them to the oven and bake at 140C/ 280F for 15 minutes. Remove them from the oven and allow them to cool. Enjoy.

Mushroom Stroganoff

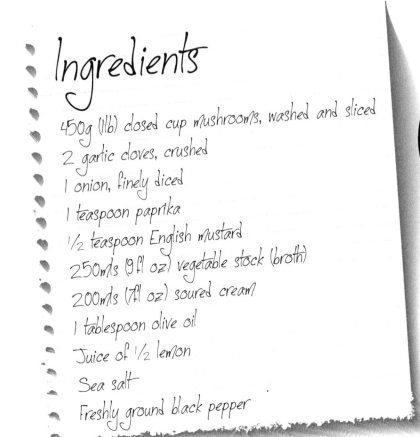

Ingredients

450g (1lb) closed cup mushrooms, washed and sliced
2 garlic cloves, crushed
1 onion, finely diced
1 teaspoon paprika
½ teaspoon English mustard
250mls (9 fl oz) vegetable stock (broth)
200mls (7 fl oz) soured cream
1 tablespoon olive oil
Juice of ½ lemon
Sea salt
Freshly ground black pepper

**SERVES
4**

165
calories
per serving

Method

Heat the oil in a frying pan and add the onion. Cook for 5 minutes until the onion softens. Add the garlic and mushrooms and cook for 5 minutes until the mushrooms are golden. Stir in the paprika and mustard and cook for 1 minute. Pour in the stock (broth) and cook for 5 minutes. Pour in the soured cream and stir well, then add in the lemon juice. Season with salt and pepper. Serve with cauliflower rice.

Chickpea, Lemon & Coriander Salad

Ingredients

400g (14oz) tin of chickpeas (garbanzo beans), drained
4 tablespoon fresh coriander (cilantro)
2 spring onions (scallions) finely chopped
1 tablespoon lemon juice
Sea salt
Freshly ground black pepper

SERVES 2

140 calories per serving

Method

Place the chickpeas (garbanzo beans) into a bowl and add in the coriander (cilantro), spring onions (scallions) and lemon juice. Mix the ingredients well. Season with salt and pepper. Eat straight away or store in the fridge until ready to use.

Garlic & Herb King Prawns

Ingredients

450g (1lb) raw king prawns, shelled
4 tablespoons fresh parsley, chopped
3 cloves of garlic, crushed
2 tablespoons olive oil
Juice of 1 lemon

SERVES 4

140
calories
per serving

Method

In a bowl, place a tablespoon of olive oil, parsley, lemon juice and garlic. Add the prawns and coat them with the mixture. Place in the fridge and marinate for 30 minutes, or longer if possible. When you're ready to cook the prawns, heat a tablespoon of olive oil in a pan. Add the prawns and cook them until for around 3-4 minutes until they are cooked through and completely pink. Serve and enjoy.

Cashew Crust Kale Chips

Ingredients

100g (3½ oz) kale leaves, chopped into bite-size pieces and stalks removed

50g (2oz) cashew nuts, soaked for 2 hours

1 tablespoon soy sauce

1 teaspoon Dijon mustard

1 teaspoon cider vinegar

Juice of ½ lemon

SERVES 2

165 calories per serving

Method

Place the cashews, lemon juice, soy sauce, mustard and vinegar into a food processor and blitz until smooth. Spread the cashew mixture onto the kale, coating it well. Scatter the kale leaves on a large baking sheet. Transfer them to the oven and bake at 180C/360F for 12-15 minutes until slightly golden. Allow them to cool before serving.

Cheddar & Spinach Mini Omelettes

SERVES 4

133 calories per serving

Ingredients

50g (2oz) Cheddar, grated (shredded)
75g (3oz) spinach leaves, finely chopped
4 large eggs

Method

Place the spinach into a steamer and cook for about 3 minutes until tender. In a bowl, whisk the eggs together then add the cheese. Stir the spinach into the mixture. Lightly grease a 4 portion muffin tin. Pour in the egg and spinach mixture. Bake in the oven at 180C/360F for around 20 minutes until the eggs are set. These can be enjoyed warm or cold.

Fish Casserole

Ingredients

250g (9oz) frozen cooked prawns, peeled
150g (5oz) fresh scallops
100g (3½ oz) mushrooms
2 x 400g (2 x 14oz) tins chopped tomatoes
2 cloves garlic, finely chopped
1 onion, finely chopped
1 red pepper (bell pepper), chopped
1 green pepper (bell pepper), chopped
1 bay leaf
1 tablespoon fresh parsley, chopped
½ teaspoon ground cumin
½ teaspoon cayenne pepper
200mls (7fl oz) chicken stock (broth)
1 tablespoon olive oil
Sea salt
Freshly ground black pepper

SERVES 4

192
calories
per serving

Method

Heat the olive oil in a large saucepan. Add the onions and cook for 4 minutes until the onion softens. Add in the mushrooms, peppers and garlic. Cook for 10 minutes, stirring occasionally. Add in the stock (broth) cumin, cayenne, tomatoes and bay leaf. Bring it to the boil, reduce the heat and simmer for 30 minutes. Add in the scallops and prawns and cook for 15 minutes. Remove the bay leaf before serving the casserole. Sprinkle in the parsley. Season with salt and pepper and serve.

Spicy Roast Chickpeas

Ingredients

400g (14oz) tin chickpeas (garbanzo beans), drained
½ teaspoon cayenne pepper
1 tablespoon olive oil
Sea salt

SERVES 2

200 calories per serving

Method

Place the olive oil, salt and cayenne pepper into a bowl and stir well. Add the chickpeas (garbanzo beans) to the bowl and coat them in the olive oil mixture. Spread the chickpeas on a baking sheet. Transfer them to the oven and bake at 220C/425F for 30 minutes or until golden. Enjoy as an anytime snack.

Rhubarb & Ginger Compote With Greek Yogurt

Ingredients

200g (7oz) plain Greek yogurt
4 stalks of rhubarb, leaves removed and roughly chopped
2cm (1inch) chunk of fresh root ginger, peeled and chopped
Zest and juice of 1 orange
1/4 teaspoon of stevia or to taste (optional)

SERVES
2

198
calories
per serving

Method

Place the rhubarb chunks in a saucepan and add in the zest and juice of the orange together with the ginger and stevia (if using). Warm in gently until the rhubarb becomes soft and pulpy. Remove it from the heat and allow it to cool. Serve the yogurt into decorative bowls and serve the rhubarb compote on top.

Peanut Butter Frozen Yogurt

Ingredients

450g (1lb) plain (unflavoured) yogurt
120mls (4 floz) milk or non-dairy milk
125g (4oz) smooth peanut butter
1 teaspoon vanilla extract
1/4 teaspoon salt
1-2 tablespoons stevia (to taste)

SERVES 2

198
calories
per serving

Method

Place all of the ingredients into an ice-cream maker and mix according to the instructions for your machine. If you don't have an ice-cream maker, transfer the mixture to a container and place it in the freezer and stir the mixture every ½ hour or so until it becomes firm. As an alternative you can add dark chocolate chips to your frozen yogurt. Delicious!

Low Carb Chocolate Brownies

Ingredients

400g (14oz) tinned black beans, drained and rinsed

75g (3oz) dark chocolate chips (min 70% cocoa)

2 tablespoons 100% cocoa powder

2 eggs

2 teaspoons pure vanilla extract

1 - 2 tablespoons stevia powder (to taste)

1/2 teaspoon cinnamon

1/2 teaspoon baking powder

Pinch of salt

75mls (3 fl oz) coconut oil

SERVES 12

146
calories
per serving

Method

Grease and line a square baking tin with parchment paper. Place all of the ingredients into a food processor and process until it becomes smooth and creamy. Spoon the batter into the lined baking tin and spread it out. Transfer it to the oven and bake at 180C/360F for 30-35 minutes. Test it with a skewer which should come out clean when the mixture is cooked. Allow it to cool. Remove it from the tin and cut into 12 squares.

Chocolate Chip Peanut Butter Cookies

Ingredients

175g (6oz) peanut butter
25g (1oz) dark chocolate chips
(min 75% cocoa)
25g (1oz) walnuts, chopped
25g (1oz) ground flaxseeds (linseeds)
1 large egg
1 teaspoon vanilla extract or seeds of
1 vanilla pod

MAKES 12

131 calories per serving

Method

Place all of the ingredients into a mixing bowl and combine them. Grease and line a baking sheet with parchment paper. Scoop out a spoonful of the mixture and place the mixture on the tray, flattening it with the back of a spoon. Repeat for the remaining mixture. Transfer it to the oven and bake at 180C/360F and cook for 15-18 minutes or until golden.

Raspberry Panna Cotta

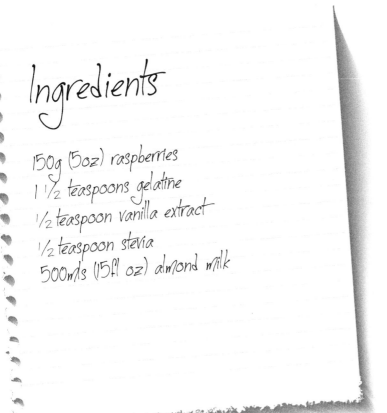

Ingredients

150g (5oz) raspberries
1 ½ teaspoons gelatine
½ teaspoon vanilla extract
½ teaspoon stevia
500mls (15fl oz) almond milk

**SERVES
4**

105
calories
per serving

Method

Pour the almond milk into a bowl and add the gelatine. Allow it to stand for 2-3 minutes until it swells. Pour the almond milk into a saucepan and stir it constantly whilst bringing it to a simmer. Stir in the stevia and vanilla and remove it from the heat. Allow it to cool. In the meantime place the raspberries in the ramekin dishes. Once the mixture has cooled, pour the almond milk mixture into the ramekin dishes. Place the dishes in the fridge for 3-4 hours to set.

Recipes Under 300 Calories

Pesto & Mozzarella Stuffed Mushrooms

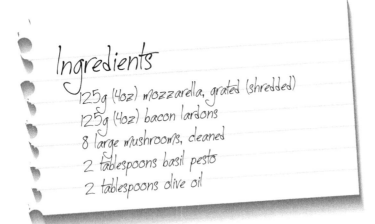

Ingredients

125g (4oz) mozzarella, grated (shredded)
125g (4oz) bacon lardons
8 large mushrooms, cleaned
2 tablespoons basil pesto
2 tablespoons olive oil

**SERVES
4**

267
calories
per serving

Method

Lay the mushrooms on a baking tray and pour a little olive oil onto each one. Sprinkle some of the bacon onto each mushroom and drizzle some pesto sauce onto each one. Top it off with a sprinkling of mozzarella. Place them in the oven at 200C/400F and cook for 8-10 minutes until the cheese is bubbling and hot. Serve with handfuls of leafy greens.

Green Goodness Smoothie

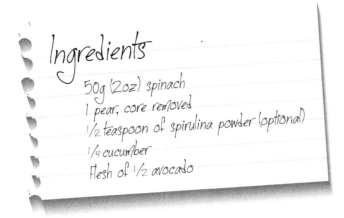

Ingredients

50g (2oz) spinach
1 pear, core removed
1/2 teaspoon of spirulina powder (optional)
1/4 cucumber
Flesh of 1/2 avocado

**SERVES
1**

242
calories
per serving

Method

Place the ingredients into a blender and pour in just enough cold water to cover them. Blitz until smooth and creamy. Serve and drink immediately.

Chunky Chicken & Vegetable Soup

Ingredients

1 whole small chicken
2.5 litres (5 pints) stock (broth)
1 onion, roughly chopped
4 carrots, roughly chopped
4 celery stalks (including leaves) roughly chopped
2 leeks, roughly chopped
1 handful of fresh parsley, chopped
2 sprigs fresh thyme
2 garlic cloves, chopped

SERVES 6

250 calories per serving

Method

Quarter the chicken into two leg portions and two breast portions and remove any excess fat from the tail and neck. Place all of the chicken in a large saucepan and add the stock (broth). Bring it to the boil, reduce the heat and simmer for 20 minutes. Using a slotted spoon, skim off any excess grease from the surface of the liquid. Now you can add in the onion, garlic, carrots, celery, leeks and thyme. Simmer gently for 1½ hours or until the chicken has completely cooked. Remove the chicken carcass and once again skim off any fat which has floated to the surface. Stir in the chopped parsley. Serve into bowls.

Oregano & Lemon Roast Chicken

Ingredients

6 sprigs of oregano, stalk removed

3 large handfuls rocket (arugula)

1 large whole chicken

2 tablespoons olive oil

Juice of 2 lemons

Sea salt

Freshly ground black pepper

1 sliced lemon

SERVES 4

244 calories per serving

Method

Place the oregano, lemon juice, olive oil, salt and pepper into a large bowl and mix well. Place the chicken into the marinade. Cover and chill in the fridge for at least 1 hour or overnight if you can. Place the chicken and marinade juices into a roasting tin and cook at 180C/360 for 1 ½ hours or until the juices of the chicken run clear when tested with a skewer. Carve the chicken and serve with slices of lemon and fresh rocket leaves. Alternatively you can serve the chicken with fresh steamed vegetables or roasted cauliflower.

Parmesan & Courgette (Zucchini) Bake

Ingredients

SERVES 4

218
calories
per serving

75g (3oz) ground almonds (almond meal/almond flour)

50g (2oz) Parmesan cheese, grated (shredded)

4 tomatoes, evenly sliced

4 courgettes (zucchinis) evenly sliced

1 teaspoon olive oil

Sea salt

Freshly ground black pepper

Method

Grease an ovenproof dish with the olive oil. Place a layer of tomatoes on the bottom of the dish. Now add a layer of courgette (zucchini). Season with salt and pepper. Sprinkle the ground almonds (almond meal/almond flour) over the top. Add a sprinkling of Parmesan cheese. Transfer it to the oven and bake at 180C/360F for 15-20 minutes until the top is golden.

Feta Cheese & Butter Bean Salad

Ingredients

- 400g (14oz) tin of butter beans
- 250g (9oz) cherry tomatoes, halved
- 125g (4oz) feta cheese, crumbled
- 75g (3oz) black olives, halved
- 2 tablespoons fresh basil, chopped
- 2 tablespoons fresh parsley, chopped
- 1 cucumber, diced
- 1 red onion, finely sliced
- 1 yellow pepper (bell pepper), diced
- 1 tablespoon olive oil
- Juice of ½ lemon

SERVES 4

279 calories per serving

Method

Place the olive oil and lemon juice in a bowl and set aside. Place all of the salad ingredients into a large bowl and mix them together. Pour on the dressing and toss the salad ingredients in the mixture.

Lemon Breadcrumb Prawns

Ingredients

400g (14oz) cooked frozen prawns, shelled and defrosted

75g (3oz) ground almonds (almond meal/ almond flour)

Zest of a lemon, grated (shredded)

1 tablespoon olive oil

Sea salt

White pepper

SERVES 4

215
calories
per serving

Method

Place the ground almonds (almond meal/almond flour) into a bowl. Add in the lemon zest and season with salt and pepper. Add the prawns to the bowl and coat them in the almond mixture. Heat the olive oil in a frying pan. Add the prawns and cook them for around 2 minutes on each side. Serve with a slice of lemon or you can add a dollop of guacamole or mayonnaise. Enjoy

Smoked Pork & Vegetable Skewers

Ingredients

SERVES 4

227 calories per serving

- 400g (14oz) pork steaks, cut into bite-sized chunks
- 1 tablespoon tomato purée (paste)
- 1 garlic clove, crushed
- 1 red pepper (bell pepper), cut into chunks
- 1 onion, cut into chunks
- 1 teaspoon smoked paprika
- 1 tablespoon lemon juice
- 1 tablespoon olive oil

Method

Place the paprika, tomato purée (paste) lemon juice, garlic and olive oil into a bowl and mix well. Add the pork pieces to the mixture and coat them thoroughly. Allow them to marinate for at least 1 hour. Thread the marinated pork, red pepper (bell pepper) and onion on skewers, alternating the ingredients. Place the skewers under a pre-heated grill (broiler) and cook for 9-10 minutes, turning during cooking until they are cooked through.

Paprika Prawn Tapas

Ingredients

300g (11oz) cooked peeled prawns
150g (5oz) chorizo sausage, chopped
3 garlic cloves, chopped
2 red chillies, deseeded, chopped
1 tablespoon smoked paprika
1 onion, finely chopped
2 tablespoons olive oil

SERVES 4

280
calories
per serving

Method

Heat the oil in a frying pan and add in the onion, garlic, chillies and paprika. Cook for 5 minutes until the onions have softened. Add in chorizo and the prawns and cook for 5 minutes. If you are using frozen prawns make sure they are hot right through. Serve by itself or with a leafy green salad.

Slow Cooker Vegetable Dahl

Ingredients

SERVES 4

286 calories per serving

300g (11oz) yellow split peas
200g (7oz) tinned chopped tomatoes
2 teaspoons ground cumin
2 teaspoons ground turmeric
2 garlic cloves, one crushed, one thinly sliced
2 teaspoons medium curry powder
1 onion, chopped
1 teaspoon ground ginger
1 red chilli, thinly sliced
600mls (1 pint) hot vegetable stock (broth)
Sea salt
Freshly ground black pepper
1 lemon, quartered, for garnish

Method

Place all of the ingredients (except salt and pepper) into a slow cooker and stir it well. Cook on high for 4 hours until tender. Season with salt and pepper. Serve with a squeeze of lemon on top. This dahl goes well with cauliflower rice as a low carb alternative to your usual white or brown rice.

Prawn & Spinach Omelette

Ingredients

200g (7oz) large cooked prawns
4 eggs, whisked
1 red chilli, finely chopped
1 garlic clove, chopped
Large handful of spinach
Juice of ½ lemon
1 tablespoon olive oil

SERVES 2

282
calories
per serving

Method

Place the eggs and lemon juice in a bowl and whisk them together. Heat half the oil in a frying pan, add the spinach, chilli and garlic and cook it for 2 minutes until it wilts. Add in the prawns and cook until they are hot throughout. Remove and set aside. Heat the remaining oil in a frying pan, pour in half of the eggs and allow them to set. Turn the omelette over and cook the other side. Serve the omelette onto a plate and spoon half of the prawn and spinach mixture into the open omelette then fold it over. Repeat for the remaining mixture.

Spiced Mackerel

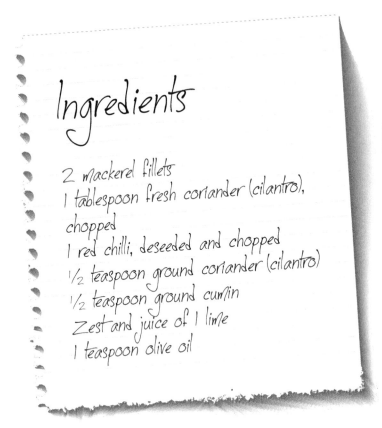

Ingredients

2 mackerel fillets
1 tablespoon fresh coriander (cilantro), chopped
1 red chilli, deseeded and chopped
½ teaspoon ground coriander (cilantro)
½ teaspoon ground cumin
Zest and juice of 1 lime
1 teaspoon olive oil

**SERVES
2**

268
calories
per serving

Method

Place the cumin, fresh and ground coriander (cilantro), chilli, zest and juice of the lime and olive oil in a bowl and mix well. Thickly coat the mackerel with the mixture. Transfer the fish to a hot grill (broiler) and cook for around 4 minutes on each side until cooked through.

Thai Chicken Soup

Ingredients

400g (14oz) skinless chicken breast fillets, cut into thin strips

150g (5oz) green beans

6 spring onions (scallions), chopped

1 tablespoon thai curry paste

900mls (1½ pints) chicken stock (broth)

1 tablespoon fish sauce

1 tablespoon olive oil

Juice of ½ lime

Sea salt

Freshly ground black pepper

Handful of fresh coriander (cilantro) leaves, roughly chopped

**SERVES
4**

215
calories
per serving

Method

Heat the oil in a large pan or wok. Add the spring onions (scallions) and cook for 2 minutes. Add in the chicken pieces and cook for 5 minutes. Stir in the thai curry paste and cook for 1 minute. Pour in the chicken stock (broth) and green beans. Bring to the boil, reduce the heat and simmer for 15 minutes. Squeeze in the lime juice and add the fish sauce. Sprinkle in the coriander (cilantro) and season with salt and pepper. Allow the coriander (cilantro) to wilt for around a minute. Serve into bowls. This is a light soup and coconut milk can be added if desired, by substituting half a pint of the stock for coconut milk.

Tuna & Chickpea Salad

Ingredients

400g (14oz) tin of chickpeas (garbanzo beans)
100g (3 ½ oz) tuna, drained
75g (3oz) broccoli, broken into florets and halved
75g (3oz) cherry tomatoes
1 red chilli (optional)
1 tablespoon capers
Juice of ½ lemon
Large bunch fresh parsley

**SERVES
2**

223
calories
per serving

Method

Place the broccoli into a steamer and cook for 3 minutes until it has softened. Remove it an allow it to cool. Place the tuna in a bowl and flake it with a fork. Add in the chickpeas (garbanzo beans) and capers and stir well. Add in the tomatoes, parsley and chilli. Once the broccoli has cooled add it to the ingredients in the bowl. Add in the lemon juice before serving.

Quick Bean Chilli

Ingredients

400g (14oz) tin of mixed beans
400g (14oz) tin of chopped tomatoes
2 teaspoons ground cumin
1 teaspoon dried oregano
½ teaspoon smoked paprika
¼ teaspoon chilli powder
Sea salt
Freshly ground black pepper

SERVES 2

250 calories per serving

Method

Place all of your ingredients into a saucepan, bring them to the boil and reduce the heat. Simmer for 10 minutes until the mixture is thoroughly warmed. Serve along with cauliflower rice and green salad.

Slow Cooked Beef Curry

Ingredients

450g (1lb) beef stewing steak, cubed
400g (14oz) tinned chopped tomatoes
2 cloves garlic, minced
1 onion, chopped
1 green chilli, finely chopped
1 tablespoon curry powder
1 teaspoon ground ginger
250mls (8fl oz) beef stock (broth)
1 tablespoon olive oil
Sea salt
Freshly ground black pepper .

SERVES 4

277 calories per serving

Method

Heat the olive oil in a frying pan and add in the beef. Cook it for several minutes then remove it together with the meat juices and set aside. Add the garlic, ginger and chilli to the pan and cook for 1 minute. Add in the tomatoes and curry powder and mix well. Add the onion to the slow cooker and add in the beef. Pour in the tomato mixture and beef stock (broth). Place the lid on the slow cooker and cook on low for around 6 hours. Season with salt and pepper. Serve with cauliflower rice or roast vegetables.

Asparagus & Poached Egg

Ingredients

150g (5oz) asparagus, tough end removed
50g (2oz) green salad leaves
1 large egg
1 tablespoon olive oil
1 tablespoon lemon juice
Sea salt
Freshly ground black pepper
1 teaspoon parmesan cheese, grated (shredded)
Dash of vinegar

SERVES 1

245 calories per serving

Method

Lay the asparagus under a pre-heated grill and cook for 5 minutes on each side. Half fill a large saucepan with water and bring it to a simmer. Add in the vinegar and stir. Crack the egg into a small side plate and slide it into the water. Cook for around 3 minutes until it firms up but remains soft in the middle. Combine the olive oil and lemon juice in a bowl and season it with salt and pepper. Coat the salad leaves with the dressing. Scatter the salad leaves on a plate, serve the asparagus on top and add the egg. Sprinkle with Parmesan cheese and eat straight away.

Chicken Cacciatore

Ingredients

250g (9 oz) mushrooms, sliced
4 chicken breasts
2 x 400g (14oz) tins of chopped tomatoes
2 green peppers (bell peppers) chopped
1 onion, finely diced
1 tablespoon tomato paste (purée)
1 teaspoon dried basil
2 cloves garlic, chopped

SERVES 4

225 calories per serving

Method

Place all ingredients in the slow cooker and stir them well. Place the lid on the slow cooker and cook for 6-7 hours. Serve with mashed cauliflower, salad or roast vegetables.

Chicken Fajitas, Salsa & Lettuce Wrap

Ingredients

FOR THE SALSA

1 red onion, finely chopped
425g (15oz) tomatoes, chopped
2 garlic cloves, crushed
Handful of fresh coriander (cilantro) leaves, chopped

FOR THE CHICKEN FAJITAS

4 large chicken breasts, cut into strips
1 red onion, thinly sliced
2 red peppers (bell peppers) thinly sliced
1 large romaine lettuce, separated into leaves
1/4 teaspoon paprika
1/4 teaspoon mild chilli powder
1/4 teaspoon ground cumin
1/4 teaspoon dried oregano
1 tablespoon olive oil

SERVES 4

258
calories
per serving

Method

FOR THE SALSA:
Place all the ingredients for the salsa into a bowl and combine them. Season with pepper. Chill in the fridge for 20 minutes.

FOR THE FAJITAS:
Heat the olive oil in a large frying pan, add the onion and peppers. Cook for 3 minutes until the vegetables begin to soften. Add in the chicken, paprika, cumin, chilli powder and oregano and stir well. Cook for around 6 minutes, or until the chicken is thoroughly cooked. Serve the chicken mixture inside a lettuce leaves and add a spoonful of salsa on top. Enjoy. You could also add guacamole or sour cream to your fajita.

Spinach, Blue Cheese & Walnut Salad

Ingredients

200g (7oz) spinach leaves, finely chopped and thick stalks removed

100g (3 ½ oz) blue cheese, crumbled

12 walnut halves

2 tablespoons fresh parsley, chopped

1 tablespoon fresh chives, chopped

2 tablespoons olive oil

2 tablespoons apple cider vinegar

SERVES 4

246 calories per serving

Method

Mix the vinegar, olive oil, spinach, chives and parsley in a bowl and coat the leaves well. Add the walnuts and blue cheese to the salad and serve.

Chocolate Mousse

Ingredients

250g (9oz) mascarpone cheese
75g (3oz) 100% cocoa powder
2 tablespoons stevia granulated sweetener
200mls (7fl oz) double cream (heavy cream)

SERVES 8

289 calories per serving

Method

Place the cocoa powder in a bowl and add a tablespoon of the cream. Stir to a paste then pour in the remaining cream. Transfer the mixture to a food processor and add in the stevia and mascarpone. Process until smooth and creamy. Serve the mousse into small dessert bowls and chill before serving.

Recipes Under
400 Calories

Moroccan Tuna Steaks

Ingredients

2 tuna steaks (approx. 2cm thick)
2 cloves of garlic
3 tablespoons fresh coriander (cilantro), chopped
1/2 teaspoon paprika
1/2 teaspoon ground cumin
1/4 teaspoon chilli powder
1 tablespoon lemon juice
2 tablespoons olive oil

SERVES 2

339 calories per serving

Method

Place the olive oil, garlic, coriander (cilantro), paprika, cumin, chilli powder and lemon juice into a food processor and blitz until smooth. Transfer the mixture to a bowl and place the tuna steaks in the marinade. Allow it to sit for 30 minutes. Heat a frying pan and add the tuna steaks. Cook for 3-6 minutes, depending on how well done you like them cooked, turning once in between. Serve and eat straight away.

Turkey & Chickpea Balls

Ingredients

400g (14oz) tin of chickpeas (garbanzo beans), rinsed and drained
250g (9oz) turkey mince (ground turkey)
50g (2oz) chickpea flour (garbanzo bean flour/gram flour)
2 tablespoons olive oil
2 garlic cloves, finely chopped
1 teaspoon cumin
½ onion, chopped
½ teaspoon baking powder
Sea salt
Freshly ground black pepper

**SERVES
4**

322
calories
per serving

Method

Place all of the ingredients, except the oil, into a food processor and mix until everything is chopped and well combined. Transfer the mixture to a bowl, cover it and chill in the fridge for around 30 minutes for the mixture to firm slightly. Take a spoonful of the mixture and using wet hands, shape it into balls. Repeat for the remaining mixture. Heat the olive oil in a frying pan, add the balls and cook them for 12-15 minutes, turning frequently until cooked through. Serve with guacamole or mayonnaise and salad.

Smoked Salmon & Pesto 'Spaghetti'

Ingredients

75g (3oz) smoked salmon, sliced
4 medium courgettes (zucchinis)
1 tablespoon pesto sauce
2 lemon wedges

SERVES 2

307
calories
per serving

Method

Prepare the courgette (zucchini) by using a spiraliser to create strips of courgette (zucchini) If you don't have a spiraliser, use a vegetable peeler and cut the strips into thin spaghetti-like lengths. Place the courgette strips into a steamer and cook for 3-4 minutes until they have softened. Once it has cooked, stir the pesto into the courgette (zucchini). Serve it into bowls and top if off with the smoked salmon. Squeeze a piece of lemon over the top and enjoy.

Aubergine & Lentil Bake

Ingredients

2 x 400g tins green lentils, drained
400g (14oz) tin chopped tomatoes
50g (2oz) Cheddar cheese, grated (shredded)
2 aubergines (eggplants), sliced
2 cloves garlic, sliced
2 teaspoons ground cinnamon
1 onion, chopped
1 egg
1 carrot, finely diced
1 bay leaf
1 tablespoon tomato puree
Small bunch or oregano, chopped
300mls (1/2 pint) plain (unflavoured) yogurt
200mls (7fl oz) vegetable stock (broth)
1 tablespoon lemon juice
1 tablespoon olive oil

SERVES 4

390 calories per serving

Method

Heat the oil in a frying pan, add the onion and cook for 4 minutes until softened. Add the lentils, carrot, stock (broth) tomatoes, garlic, purée, oregano, cinnamon, lemon juice and bay leaf. Bring it to the boil, reduce the heat and simmer for 30 minutes. In the meantime place the aubergine slices under a preheated grill (broiler) and cook on both sides until slightly golden. In a bowl, combine the yogurt, cheese and egg. When the lentil mixture has completely cooked, spoon half of the mixture into an ovenproof lasagne dish and place a layer of aubergine (eggplant) on top. Add a second layer of the lentil mixture and add another layer of aubergine. Spread the yogurt mixture on top. Transfer it to the oven and bake at 180C/360F for 45 minutes and cook until golden.

Rosemary Chicken & Roast Vegetables

SERVES 4

318 calories per serving

Ingredients

250g (9oz) cherry tomatoes, halved

4 chicken breasts

1 aubergine (eggplant, roughly chopped

2 courgettes (zucchinis), roughly chopped

2 red peppers (bell peppers), sliced

1 green pepper (bell pepper), sliced

4 sprigs of fresh rosemary

2 cloves of garlic, chopped

2 tablespoons olive oil

Method

In a large ovenproof dish, spread the aubergine (eggplant), tomatoes, courgettes, (zucchinis) and peppers (bell peppers) with 2 sprigs of rosemary, 1 clove of garlic and a tablespoon of olive oil. Transfer it to the oven and cook at 200C/400F for 20 minutes. In the meantime, mix the remaining garlic, rosemary and olive oil in a bowl. Make an incision in the chicken breasts and spread some of the mixture into each one. Once the vegetables have been in for 20 minutes, add the chicken breasts to the dish. Return it to the oven and cook for another 20 minutes or until the chicken is thoroughly cooked.

Parsley & Lemon Salmon

Ingredients

50g (2oz) spinach leaves
2 salmon fillets
2 tablespoons fresh parsley, chopped
2 tablespoons olive oil
1 clove of garlic
Juice of 1 lemon
Freshly ground black pepper

SERVES 2

400 calories per serving

Method

Mix together the lemon juice, 2 tablespoons olive oil, garlic and parsley and season with pepper. Place the fish on a plate and lightly coat it with a tablespoon of the lemon and parsley mixture. Heat a frying pan and add the salmon. Cook for 3-4 minutes on each side and check that it's completely cooked. Scatter the spinach leaves onto plates. Serve the fish on top and spoon over the remaining lemon and parsley dressing. Enjoy.

Lentil & Bacon Soup

Ingredients

400g (14oz) tin chopped tomatoes

200g (7oz) red lentils

6 rashers smoked streaky bacon, chopped

2 carrots, peeled and diced

1 onion, peeled and chopped

1.5 litres (2½ pints) vegetable stock (broth)

2 tablespoons chopped fresh parsley

1 tablespoon olive oil

SERVES 4

302 calories per serving

Method

Heat the oil in a large saucepan. Add the bacon, onion and carrots and cook over a medium heat, stirring occasionally, for 8-10 minutes, or until the bacon has started to turn golden and the vegetables have softened. Add the lentils to the pan and stir well. Add the chopped tomatoes and the stock (broth). Bring to the boil, cover, and then simmer the soup gently for about 1 hour, or until the lentils are tender. Sprinkle in the parsley. Allow the soup to cool slightly then using a hand blender or food processor blitz the soup is smooth. Serve into bowls.

Green Lentil Curry

Ingredients

125g (4oz) green lentils
100g (3½ oz) spinach leaves
25g (1oz) fresh coriander (cilantro) chopped
2 cloves of garlic, chopped
1 onion, chopped
1 red chilli, finely chopped
1 carrot, chopped
1 tablespoon tomato purée (tomato paste)
1-2 teaspoons curry powder
200mls (7 fl oz) coconut milk
360mls (12 fl oz) vegetable stock (broth)
1 teaspoon coconut oil

SERVES 2

315
calories
per serving

Method

Heat the coconut oil in a frying pan and add the carrot and onion. Cook for 5 minutes until the vegetables have softened. Add the chilli and garlic and cook for 1 minute. Stir in the lentils, tomato purée and the curry powder. Cover and cook for 2 minutes. Pour in the coconut milk and the vegetable stock (broth) bring it to the boil then reduce the heat and cover it. Simmer for 30 minutes. Add in the spinach and stir until it has softened. Sprinkle in the coriander (cilantro) and enjoy.

Mexican Chunky Soup

Ingredients

400g (14oz) tin cannellini beans, drained and rinsed
200g (7oz) chorizo sausage, sliced
3 large carrots, peeled and diced
1 onion, peeled and finely chopped
1 garlic clove, crushed
1 teaspoon chilli powder
1 red pepper (bell pepper), chopped
1 green pepper (bell pepper), chopped
600mls (1 pint) warm vegetable stock (broth)
1 tablespoon olive oil
Salt and freshly ground black pepper

**SERVES
4**

355
calories
per serving

Method

Heat the oil in a large saucepan, add the chorizo and cook for 3 minutes. Remove it and set aside. Add in the onion, garlic and carrots. Cover and cook gently for about 5 minutes, stirring occasionally. Add in the chilli powder and vegetable stock (broth) and bring to the boil. Return the chorizo to the sauce and add in the peppers (bell peppers) and cannellini beans. Season with salt and pepper. Serve into bowls.

Beef Goulash

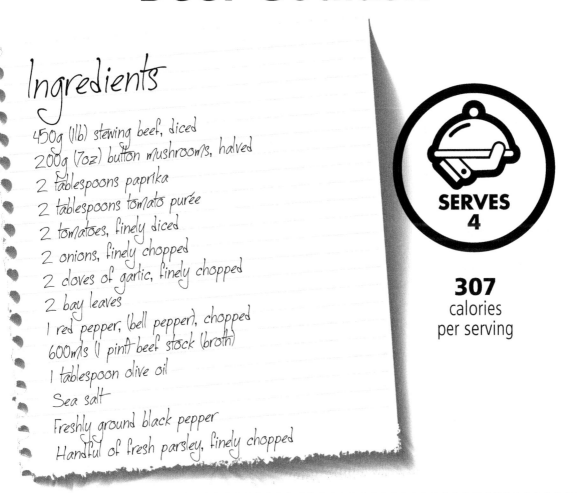

Ingredients

450g (1lb) stewing beef, diced
200g (7oz) button mushrooms, halved
2 tablespoons paprika
2 tablespoons tomato purée
2 tomatoes, finely diced
2 onions, finely chopped
2 cloves of garlic, finely chopped
2 bay leaves
1 red pepper, (bell pepper), chopped
600mls (1 pint) beef stock (broth)
1 tablespoon olive oil
Sea salt
Freshly ground black pepper
Handful of fresh parsley, finely chopped

SERVES 4

307 calories per serving

Method

Place the beef in a bowl and add in the paprika. Stir them together and coat the beef really well. Heat the olive oil in a large saucepan and add the beef. Stir and cook it until its browned. Add the onions and garlic to the saucepan and cook for 5 minutes. Return the beef to the saucepan and add in the tomatoes, tomato purée (paste) and bay leaves. Cook for 5 minutes. Pour in the stock (broth) then leave to simmer on a low heat for 2 hours. Remember to check the liquid during cooking and add extra stock if you need to. Stir in the mushrooms and peppers and cook for 15 minutes. Sprinkle in the parsley and stir. Season with salt and pepper. Remove the bay leaves before serving.

Turkish Eggs

Ingredients

400g (14oz) tinned chopped tomatoes
2 eggs
1 onion, finely chopped
1 red pepper (bell pepper), finely chopped
1/2 red chilli, finely chopped (more if you like a spicy sauce)
1 clove of garlic, crushed
1/4 teaspoon ground cumin
1/4 teaspoon paprika
1 teaspoon olive oil
Handful of fresh parsley, finely chopped
Sea salt
Freshly ground black pepper

SERVES 1

358 calories per serving

Method

Heat the olive oil in a frying pan. Add the onion, garlic and red pepper (bell pepper) and cook for 5 minutes until they soften. Add in the tomatoes, chilli, cumin and paprika. Season with salt and black pepper. Reduce the heat and cook gently for 5 minutes. Crack each of the eggs on top of the tomato mixture and allow them to cook until the eggs are done to your liking. Sprinkle with parsley and serve.

Eggs With Carrot & Bacon Hash

Ingredients

3 rashers of streaky bacon, finely chopped

2 eggs

1 large carrot, grated

½ onion, finely chopped

1 teaspoon olive oil

Freshly ground black pepper

SERVES 1

352
calories
per serving

Method

Heat the oil in a frying pan, add the bacon and onion and cook for 4-5 minutes. Stir in the carrot and cook for 10 minutes. In the meantime, place the eggs into a saucepan of warm water and boil them for 6-7 minutes until the yolks are slightly soft. Season the hash with black pepper and serve it onto plates. Peel and halve the eggs and place them on top of the hash. Eat immediately.

BLT Chicken Salad

Ingredients

450g (1lb) cooked chicken breasts
175g (6oz) cherry tomatoes, halved
12 romaine lettuce leaves
4 slices of bacon, cooked
2 sticks celery, chopped
2 spring onions (scallions) chopped
1 avocado, flesh removed and diced
1 tablespoon chopped fresh parsley
1 teaspoon fresh lemon juice
2 tablespoons mayonnaise
Sea salt
Freshly ground black pepper

SERVES 4

340 calories per serving

Method

In a bowl, place the mayonnaise, spring onions (scallions), lemon juice and parsley and mix well. Season with salt and pepper. Add the chicken, bacon, celery and tomatoes to the mixture and stir well. Spoon the mixture into the lettuce leaves and top it off with chunks of avocado. Enjoy.

Sausage & Kale Stir-Fry

Ingredients

100g (3½ oz) good quality sausage, chopped
3 large kale leaves
½ onion, chopped
½ red pepper (bell pepper), chopped
Sea salt
Freshly ground black pepper

SERVES 1

332
calories
per serving

Method

Heat a frying pan, add the sausage and cook for 5 minutes or until completely brown. Add in the onion and cook for 4 minutes. Next add in the kale and red pepper (bell pepper) and cook until the vegetables have softened. Season with salt and pepper. Serve and eat immediately.

Spiced Citrus & Olive Pork

Ingredients

150g (5oz) pitted green olives
450g (1lb) pork steaks, cut into chunks
2 cloves of garlic, crushed
2 lemons, sliced and seeds removed
1 onion, finely chopped
1 teaspoon ground ginger
1 teaspoon ground coriander (cilantro)
2 teaspoons turmeric
1 tablespoon olive oil
450mls (15fl oz) chicken stock (broth)
Handful of fresh parsley, chopped
Sea salt
Freshly ground black pepper

SERVES 4

304 calories per serving

Method

Heat the oil in a large saucepan. Add the onion and cook for 5 minutes until it softens. Add the garlic, ginger, coriander (cilantro) and turmeric and cook for 1 minute. Add the pork pieces and cook for 5 minutes, stirring occasionally. Add the sliced lemons and the stock (broth). Season with salt and pepper. Bring it to the boil, reduce the heat and simmer gently for 30 minutes. Add the olives and cook for a further 3 minutes. Stir in the parsley. This dish can be served with salad, cauliflower rice or courgette spaghetti.

Lamb Skewers & Yogurt Dip

Ingredients

450g (1lb) boneless lamb steaks
150g (5oz) plain (unflavoured) yogurt
2 teaspoons ground cumin
1 teaspoon turmeric
1 teaspoon ground coriander (cilantro)
Juice of 1 lemon

YOGURT DIP
250g (9oz) natural yogurt (unflavoured)
1 fresh mint, chopped
1 small onion, finely sliced
1/4 teaspoon cumin

SERVES 4

316
calories
per ball

Method

Chop the lamb into bite-size chunks. In a bowl, combine the 150g (5oz) yogurt, cumin, turmeric, coriander (cilantro) and lemon juice. Add the lamb to the marinade, cover it and place it in the fridge for one hour. In the meantime, to make the yogurt dip, combine the 250g (9oz) yogurt, chopped onion, mint and cumin. Chill it in the fridge. Once the lamb is marinated, thread the lamb chunks onto skewers. Place under a hot grill (broiler) for 5 minutes on either side. Serve with the dip.

Tandoori Salmon

Ingredients

2 salmon steaks
2cm (1 inch) chunk of fresh ginger root,
peeled and finely chopped
2 cloves of garlic, crushed
2 teaspoons paprika
1/2 teaspoon ground cumin
1/2 teaspoon ground coriander (cilantro)
1/4 teaspoon cayenne pepper (or more to taste)
100g (3 1/2 oz) Greek yogurt

**SERVES
2**

350
calories
per serving

Method

Place all of the ingredients, except the salmon, into a bowl and mix them well. Marinate the salmon in the mixture for at least 1 hour but preferably overnight to allow it to infuse. Place the salmon on a baking tray and cook it in the oven at 200C/400F for 40-45 minutes, or until the salmon is cooked through. Serve with a large green leafy salad.

Recipes Under 550 Calories

Mustard Lime Turkey & Butter Bean Mash

Ingredients

400g (14oz) tin of butter beans, drained and rinsed

50g (2oz) spinach leaves

2 turkey fillets

2 tablespoons crème fraîche

1 garlic clove, crushed

1 teaspoon wholegrain mustard

Juice of ½ lime

Sea salt

Freshly ground black pepper

SERVES 2

411 calories each

Method

Place the lime juice and mustard in a bowl and mix together. Add the turkey steaks and coat them well. Place the turkey steaks under a hot grill (broiler) and cook for 5-6 minutes on each side until thoroughly cooked. In the meantime place the butter beans in a saucepan and add in the garlic and crème fraîche. Season with salt and pepper. Warm the beans thoroughly. Remove the beans from the heat and mash them. Scatter the spinach leaves onto a plate. Spoon the mash on top and add the turkey steak.

Chinese Chicken Salad

Ingredients

FOR THE DRESSING:

2 tablespoons tahini paste (sesame seed paste)
1 clove of garlic, finely chopped
1 tablespoon soy sauce
2 tablespoons fresh lemon juice
Sea salt
Freshly ground black pepper

FOR THE SALAD:

2 skinless chicken breasts, cooked
12 cm (5 in) piece cucumber, cut into fine strips
2 carrots, cut into fine strips
1 red pepper (bell pepper), cut into fine strips
2 Little Gem lettuces, separated into leaves
Small handful of fresh basil leaves, finely shredded
Small handful of fresh mint leaves, finely shredded
8 spring onions (scallions), halved lengthways
125g (4 oz) button mushrooms, finely sliced

SERVES 2

514
calories
per serving

Method

Place the tahini (sesame seed paste), garlic, soy sauce and lemon juice into a bowl and mix well. Season with salt and pepper. Arrange the salad ingredients onto a serving plate. Scatter over the shredded basil and mint. Cut the chicken into strips and scatter it on top. Pour the dressing into a small bowl and serve on the side.

Chicken, Cannellini & Almond Bake

Ingredients

450g (1lb) chicken thighs, skin removed
400g (14oz) tin of cannellini beans
50g (2oz) almonds, roughly chopped
2 onions, cut into quarters
2 red peppers, (bell peppers), sliced
2 garlic clove, finely chopped
1 teaspoon ground cumin
1 teaspoon smoked paprika
2 tablespoons olive oil
Juice and zest of 1 lemon

SERVES 4

488
calories
per serving

Method

Place the chicken in a large bowl along with the cannellini beans, onion, peppers and garlic. In a separate bowl, place the garlic, cumin, paprika, olive oil and lemon zest and juice. Mix it well then scoop the mixture into the bowl with the chicken and coat everything with the dressing. Transfer it to a large oven-proof dish and cook in the oven at 180C/ 360F for 45 minutes. Sprinkle in the almonds and cook for another 5 minutes. Serve and enjoy.

High Protein Blueberry Pancakes

Ingredients

SERVES 2

448
calories
per serving

100g (3½ oz) ground almonds (almond meal/almond flour)
75g (3oz) blueberries
2 eggs
1 teaspoon baking powder
60mls (2fl oz) water
1 tablespoon olive oil

Method

Put the eggs in a bowl, whisk them and set aside. Place the almond flour and baking powder in a bowl and stir in the beaten eggs. Add water and mix until you have a smooth batter. Heat the olive oil in a frying pan. Pour half of the mixture into the pan. Scatter half the blueberries in the pancake mixture and cook until the underside is slightly golden before turning and cooking until completely set and cooked through. Repeat for the remaining mixture.

Chicken & Avocado Wraps

Ingredients

50g (2oz) cooked kidney beans, rinsed and drained

1 cooked chicken breast, finely chopped

1/4 cucumber, peeled, deseeded and chopped

Flesh of 1/2 avocado

Juice 1/4 lemon

1 teaspoon olive oil

4 little gem lettuce leaves

SERVES 1

444 calories per serving

Method

Place the avocado, olive oil and lemon juice in a food processor and mix until smooth and creamy. Put the chicken, kidney beans and cucumber in a bowl and add the avocado mixture. Stir it well to combine it. Scoop some of the mixture into each of the lettuce leaves. Eat straight away.

Chicken Goujons

Ingredients

50g (2oz) ground almonds (almond flour/almond meal)
25g (1oz) sesame seeds
2 chicken breasts, cut into strips

1 egg
1/2 teaspoon ground cumin
1/2 teaspoon smoked paprika
1/2 teaspoon sea salt
1/4 teaspoon freshly ground black pepper
1 tablespoon olive oil

SERVES 2

516
calories
per serving

Method

Place the egg into a bowl and whisk it. In a separate bowl combine the ground almonds, cumin, paprika, sesame seeds, salt and pepper. Dip each piece of chicken in the egg then dip it in the dry mixture. Lay the goujons onto a plate, taking care that they don't stick together. Heat the olive oil in a large frying pan and add the goujons. Cook for 6-8 minutes, turning once halfway through. Place them on kitchen paper to drain off excess oil. Can be eaten on their own or serve with guacamole, sour cream dip or garlic mayonnaise.

Pine Nut & Avocado Courgetti

SERVES 1

524 calories each

Ingredients

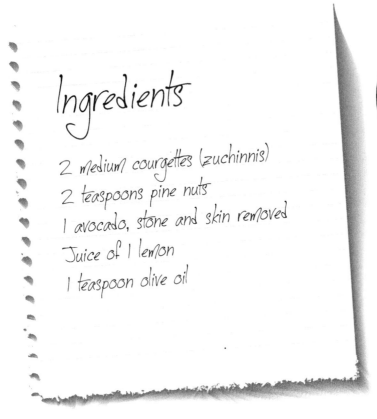

2 medium courgettes (zuchinnis)
2 teaspoons pine nuts
1 avocado, stone and skin removed
Juice of 1 lemon
1 teaspoon olive oil

Method

Use a spiraliser to spiral the courgette (zucchini) into spaghetti lengths. If you don't have a spiraliser, use a vegetable peeler and cut the strips into thin spaghetti-like lengths. Place the avocado, lemon juice and olive oil in a blender and process until it becomes creamy. Spoon the avocado mixture into the spiralised courgette. Serve onto a plate and sprinkle with pine nuts. So simple and really delicious.

Chunky Lamb Stew

Ingredients

450g (1lb) lamb steaks, cubed
2 x 400g (14oz) tin of butter beans
2 carrots, coarsely chopped
2 leeks, chopped
1 onion, coarsely chopped
1 teaspoon dried rosemary
400mls (14fl oz) vegetable stock (broth)
1 tablespoon olive oil

SERVES 4

464 calories per serving

Method

Heat the oil in a saucepan and add in the lamb. Cook for 5 minutes then stir in the carrots, onion and leeks. Cook for a further 5 minutes. Add in the vegetable stock and rosemary. Cover the saucepan and cook on a low heat for around 1 hours. Add in the butter beans and cook for another 20 minutes. Serve and enjoy.

Sirloin Steak & Chimchurri Sauce

Ingredients

FOR THE CHIMCHURRI SAUCE
50g (2oz) fresh parsley leaves
15g (1/2 oz) fresh oregano leaves
1 clove garlic
1/2 chopped red onion
1/4 teaspoon smoked paprika
1/4 teaspoon chilli pepper flakes
1/2 teaspoon sea salt
4 tablespoons olive oil
3 tablespoons red wine vinegar

FOR THE STEAK
2 sirloin steaks (approx. 5oz)
1 teaspoon olive oil
Sea salt
Freshly ground black pepper

SERVES 2

487 calories per serving

Method

FOR THE SAUCE:

Heat the oil in a frying pan, add the paprika and cook for 2 minutes. Remove from the heat and allow to cool. Place the parsley, onion, oregano, sea salt, garlic and chilli flakes in a food processor and combine them. Pour in the oil and vinegar and process until well blended.

FOR THE STEAK:

Season the steak with salt and pepper. Heat the olive oil in a frying pan. Add the steaks and cook to your liking. For rare steaks allow 1 ½ minutes each side. Medium rare 2 minutes each side and medium 2 ¼ minutes on each side Allow them to rest. Serve with the chimchurri sauce.

Halloumi, Mushroom & Tomato Kebabs

Ingredients

200g (7oz) halloumi cheese, cut into 2cm (1 inch) chunks
8 button mushrooms
2 tablespoons fresh chopped coriander (cilantro)
1 red pepper (bell pepper), cut into chunks
1 red onion, cut into chunks
1 clove of garlic, crushed
1 tablespoon olive oil
Juice of 1 lime
Freshly ground black pepper

SERVES 2

424
calories
per serving

Method

Place the olive oil, coriander (cilantro), garlic and lime into a bowl and mix well. Season with black pepper. Add the halloumi, mushrooms, onion and red pepper (bell pepper) and allow it to marinate for around 1 hour. Thread the ingredients onto skewers alternating them until everything has been used up. Place the kebabs under a preheated grill (broiler) for 10-12 minutes, turning once halfway through. Serve with a green leafy salad.

Avocado Fries

Ingredients

25g (1oz) ground almonds (almond meal/almond flour)

1 avocado

1 egg

1/2 teaspoon onion powder

1/4 teaspoon chilli powder

1/4 teaspoon sea salt

1 teaspoon olive oil

SERVES 1

538 calories per serving

Method

Halve the avocado and remove the stone and the skin. Cut it into slices of around 1-2cms thick. Whisk the egg in a bowl and set aside. Place the ground almonds (almond meal/almond flour) into a bowl and add the onion powder, chilli and salt. Dip the avocado slices in the beaten egg and then dip it in the almond mixture, coating them well. Coat a baking sheet with olive oil and lay the avocado slices on it. Transfer it to the oven and cook for 15-20 minutes at 180C/360F, turning the slices half way through and cooking until slightly golden. Serve and eat straight away.

Chickpea & Chorizo Casserole

Ingredients

450g (1lb) skinless chicken thighs
400g (14oz) tin of chopped tomatoes
225g (8oz) chickpeas (garbanzo beans), drained
100g (3½ oz) chorizo, cut into bite-sized chunks
3 cloves garlic, chopped
2 red peppers (bell peppers), chopped
2 teaspoons ground coriander (cilantro)
1 onion, chopped
200ml (7fl oz) chicken stock (broth)
1 tablespoon olive oil
Sea salt
Freshly ground black pepper

SERVES 4

428 calories per serving

Method

Heat the oil in a frying pan, add the chicken thighs and cook until golden. Remove them from the pan and set aside. Add the chorizo to the oil and cook for 2 minutes. Add in the onions, garlic, red peppers (bell peppers) and coriander (cilantro) and cook for 3 minutes. Pour in the chopped tomatoes, chickpeas (garbanzo beans) and the stock (broth) and add the chicken thighs. Bring it to the boil and simmer for 25 minutes. Season with salt and pepper. Serve with roast vegetables.

Southern Pork & Beans

Ingredients

400g (14oz) tin chopped tomatoes
2 x 400g (14oz) tins cannellini beans, drained
250g (9oz) pork tenderloin fillet, diced
150g (5oz) gammon steak, diced
2 tablespoons tomato purée (paste)
2 teaspoons English mustard
2cm (1 inch) chunk of ginger, finely chopped
2 garlic cloves, finely chopped
2 teaspoons smoked paprika
1 small handful of parsley, chopped
1 onion, sliced
1/2 teaspoon hot chilli powder
4 tablespoons plain yogurt
400ml (14fl oz) chicken stock (broth)
1 tablespoon olive oil
Sea salt
Freshly ground black pepper

**SERVES
4**

469
calories
per serving

Method

Heat the olive oil in a large frying pan, add the onion and cook for 4 minutes. Stir in the pork and gammon and cook for 3 minutes. Add the garlic, ginger, paprika and chilli powder and cook for 30 seconds or so before adding in the tomatoes and beans. Mix really well. Add in the tomato purée (paste) and mustard. Pour over the stock (broth) and simmer for 25 minutes, stirring occasionally, until the pork is completely cooked and tender. Stir in the yogurt and half of the parsley and warm it through. Season with salt and pepper. Serve with an extra sprinkling of parsley.

You may also be interested in other titles by
Erin Rose Publishing
which are available in both paperback and ebook.

 Quick Start Guides

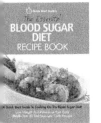   

  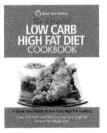 

Books by Sophie Ryan
Erin Rose Publishing

30 Simple And Delicious Superfood Energy Balls And Bites
Recipes For Great Health and Wellbeing

Over 30 Easy And Delicious Superfood Energy Bars
Recipes To Boost Your Vitality

30 Simple And Tasty Energy Shots And Smoothies
To Power Up Your Health And Well-Being